STRING

MW00619285

By
MICHELE LOWE

Dramatic Publishing
Woodstock, Illinois • England • Australia • New Zealand

*** NOTICE ***

IMPORTANT BILLING AND CREDIT REQUIREMENTS

STRING OF PEARLS was produced by City Theatre Company (Tracy Brigden, artistic director; David Jobin, managing director) in Pittsburgh in October 2003. It was directed by Eric Simonson; the set design was by Loy Arcenas; the costume design was by Michael Olich; the lighting design was by Thomas C. Hase; the sound design was by Dave Bjornson and the stage manager was Patti Kelly. The cast was as follows:

WOMAN #1 . . . . Rebecca Harris
WOMAN #2 . . . . Helena Ruoti
WOMAN #3 . . . . Sheila McKenna
WOMAN #4 . . . . Sharon Washington

STRING OF PEARLS was produced by Primary Stages (Casey Childs, executive producer; Andrew Leynse, artistic director, Elliot Fox, managing director) in New York City in September 2004. It was directed by Eric Simonson; the set design was by Loy Arcenas; the costume design was by David Zinn, the lighting design was by D.M. Wood, the sound design was by Lindsay Jones and the stage manager was Emily N. Wells. The cast was as follows:

WOMAN #1 . . . . Ellen McLaughlin
WOMAN #2 . . . . Mary Testa
WOMAN #3 . . . . Antoinette LaVecchia
WOMAN #4 . . . . Sharon Washington

STRING OF PEARLS was commissioned and developed by The Cherry Lane Theatre, New York City; and received further development from New York Stage and Film, The Powerhouse Theatre at Vassar College.

Special thanks to Matt Williams and Pamela Perrell.

STRING OF PEARLS

An ensemble piece for 4 women playing 27 roles

CHARACTERS (in order of appearance)

AMY . . . . 35, a research scientist living in Saddle River
in the present
BETH . . . . 39, a housewife living in Saddle River in 1969
The same actress also plays Beth when she is 74
ELA . . . . . 42, a divorced mother of two living near Milwaukee
in 1981
HELEN . . . . 40, a political consultant living in San Diego
in 1982
STEPHANIE. . . . . 44, an architect/mother living in Boston
in 1982
JOSIANNE . . . . 30, a Tunisian hotel maid living in Escondido,
Calif., in 1982
DORA . . . . 53, a chaperone for the New York City Ballet
living in Manhattan in 1983
VICTORIA . . . . . . 40, a housewife living in Manhattan in 1995
ABBY . . . . 38, a money manager living in Manhattan
in the present
KYLE . . . . . 46, a mortician's assistant living in New York City
in the present
CINDY . . 45, a gravedigger living in Nyack, N.Y., in the present
HALLIE. . . . . Beth's housekeeper
ROBERTA . . . . Amy's friend
BEVERLY . . . . Poughkeepsie housewife
LINDA . . . . Beth's daughter
WANDA. . . . . an old friend of Ela's
RANDY . . . . another old friend of Ela's

DENISE. . . . . Ela's sister-in-law
ZOE . . . . Stephanie's 3-year-old-daughter
AUNT PATTY . . . . Josianne's aunt
ERICA . . . . woman on the beach
JITTERS . . . . . . 20, a Latina art student going to Paris to study
FRENCH SALESWOMAN
GLORIA. . . . . Abby's mother
JEWELER
CHERYLE . . . . school cafeteria worker living in the Bronx
KYLE'S MOTHER

The Breakdown

Woman One
Amy, Wanda, Helen, Aunt Patty, Jitters, Abby

Woman Two
Beth, Randy, Denise, Josianne, Victoria, Kyle's Mother

Woman Three
Hallie, Linda, Stephanie, Dora, Cheryle, Gloria, Jeweler, Cindy

Woman Four
Roberta, Beverly, Ela, Zoe, French Saleswoman, Erica, Kyle

AUTHOR'S NOTES

STRING OF PEARLS was originally conceived as a piece for four actresses to show their immeasurable talent. It is my hope that an imaginative and non-traditional casting policy be used when casting STRING OF PEARLS in order to affirm the participation of women of all ethnic backgrounds.

A FINAL NOTE: the character Josianne says "dollar" instead of "dollars." It is not a misprint in the script.

STRING OF PEARLS

2004

AT RISE: *Music. The stage is bare, dark. Lights up on BETH, 74.*

BETH *(to us)*. My granddaughter Amy is marrying Kevin. She is living with me until the wedding. I have lived alone for thirty-five years. I am not used to seeing an extra plate in the sink or smelling sandalwood and vetiver in the hall or listening at night for someone's key in the door. I like it. I like it a lot.

(HALLIE enters holding an open box.)

HALLIE. The caterer's on the phone for Amy.
BETH. She went to work. Did the florist call?
HALLIE. Not yet. *(Off the box.)* More books.
BETH. Which ones?
HALLIE. *The Life and Lyrics of Sir Edward Dyer* and *The Joy of Pickling*.
BETH *(to us)*. I'm thinking of doing some pickling.
HALLIE. Where do you want them?
BETH. Under the sink.
HALLIE. The sink?
BETH. What did I say?
HALLIE *(to us)*. She's not getting enough sleep. She stays up all night reading.

BETH. I'm not tired.

HALLIE *(to us)*. She's seventy-four. *(HALLIE exits.)*

BETH. I'm fine. I'm just excited. *(To us.)* Amy works at the hospital every night until midnight. I wait up for her. I don't mean to. Yes, I do.

(AMY enters holding her finger.)

AMY. Ow! I can't believe I did it again.

BETH. Kevin called—and so did Roberta.

AMY. Thanks, Gramma.

BETH. It's so crazy around here.

AMY. I need a Band-aid. *(AMY exits.)*

BETH *(to us)*. Amy is a doctor of some reputation. She is developing a new heart made of pig guts with a team at Mount Sinai. Amy's work is so complex, so demanding, so dangerous that the heart won't be ready for another ten years. And yet—

(AMY enters.)

AMY. Do you have any alcohol?

BETH *(to us)*. She can't sew. *(BETH exits.)*

AMY *(to us)*. I am sewing my wedding dress by hand. I work each morning from four to six. It is only half done. I am terrified that when I walk down the aisle the dress will come apart and I will have to get married naked.

(ROBERTA enters.)

ROBERTA. Do you want me to give you a shower?

AMY. A bridal shower? No.

ROBERTA. I could make it small—
AMY. No.
ROBERTA. A dozen girls at my apartment—
AMY. No, please, Roberta.
ROBERTA. When you come over for dinner next Tues-
day—?
AMY. Yes?
ROBERTA. Act surprised.

(HALLIE enters.)

HALLIE. Are you going to throw your bouquet?
ROBERTA. Are you going to write your vows?
HALLIE. Are you going to hire a band?

(BETH enters.)

BETH. Are you going to wear my pearls with your dress?
AMY. What? *(HALLIE and ROBERTA exit.)*
BETH. The pearls.
AMY *(to us)*. It is the first time she mentions the pearls.
BETH. The ones I gave your mother.
AMY *(to us)*. My mother died when I was six.
BETH. The ones she wore to her wedding.
AMY. I don't have them.
BETH. Are you sure?
AMY. Mom didn't give them to me.
BETH. Maybe your father has them.
AMY. I don't think so, Gramma—
BETH. I'll call him. *(BETH exits.)*
AMY. Gramma, don't— *(To us.)* I am ignoring my father,
I am barely speaking to my stepmother, I am enjoying

my brother Jonathan for the first time in my life. Kevin and I don't want children. We don't want a kitchen or plants. We have agreed to spend our energies on our work and on each other.

(BETH enters.)

BETH. Your father doesn't have them.
AMY *(to us)*. I have my mother's eyes, my mother's chin, and my mother's allergy to cats. I do not, however, have her pearls.
BETH. You need the pearls to get married.
AMY. The only thing I need to get married is Kevin. And the dress. *(AMY exits.)*
BETH *(to us)*. Amy retreats to her room. As the wedding draws near she speaks to me less, until the house is wrapped in silence. The replies flood the mailbox but she leaves them unopened. She reminds me of Ethan— absent, disconnected, nervous. Secretly I'm afraid she'll throw in the towel and elope. *(BETH exits.)*

(AMY enters.)

AMY. Gramma leaves a pile of my parents' wedding pictures on my pillow. I see the pearls for the first time. White, shiny, round as marbles.

(BETH enters.)

BETH. Maybe she loaned them to a friend.
AMY. Maybe she gave them back to you. *(To us.)* Cruel. I know.

BETH *(to us)*. I clean out every closet, I open every box—
AMY *(to us)*. I hear her in the middle of the night—
BETH *(to us)*. I find my engagement ring. Too big for my hands. I'm shrinking, fading, turning to dust already.
AMY *(to us)*. I resolve to be nice to her.
BETH. Maybe your brother knows where the pearls are.
AMY. I do not need the pearls to get married!
BETH *(to us)*. She doesn't understand.
AMY. What do I say?
BETH *(to us)*. How to explain?
AMY. They're lost.
BETH. If I could find them for you.
AMY. It doesn't matter—
BETH. If I could start at the beginning—
AMY. You won't find them.
BETH. Beginning with the first...
AMY *(to us)*. Before they were my mother's they were hers.
BETH. First to receive them, first to wear them, first to give them away.
AMY *(to us)*. She was thirty-nine. August 1969. *(AMY exits.)*

(We hear audio from the Apollo 11 moon landing as the lights change.)

NEIL ARMSTRONG *(voiceover)*. "Houston, Tranquility Base here. The eagle has landed."
CHARLES DUKE *(voiceover)*. "Roger, Tranquility. We copy you on the ground. You got a bunch of guys about to turn blue. We're breathing again."

(BETH is now thirty-nine. It is 1969.)

BETH. Ethan quit playing tennis after he broke his foot. He rarely rode his bike. He sat for hours in front of the television watching the moon landing. He'd do anything not to come to bed. At ten o'clock he'd call his mother in Poughkeepsie. At midnight he'd read an entire *Time*, or *Life*, or *Look*. I'd wait up for him, but it was no use. I'd pass out and by six the next morning, he was gone. Linda would see him waving to her as he went down the hall. If I woke up in the middle of the night and I touched his belly or his thigh, he'd grunt and roll over. So I'd go downstairs and turn on Channel 9.

(Music up: Jimi Hendrix's "Are You Experienced?")

I'd see all these girls on the news half-naked, dancing, feathers in their hair, belts around the hips, shaking and swaying and all I could think was—these girls were having sex. Why wasn't I?

So after dinner one night, when Linda was out at a party, I tried to talk to Ethan about how I was feeling—but all that came out was "feather" and "halter-top" and he didn't know what I was talking about. So I gave up.

Then came the invitation to his twentieth high-school reunion. All of his friends from Poughkeepsie started calling and I guess they shamed him into it, because the next thing I knew, we were going, too. And when he gave me money for a dress—I took it as a sign. Maybe he wanted to look at me like he used to. Maybe he wanted to have some fun, some feeling, some attachment—like we used to.

I went to Bonwit Teller and bought a flaming-red, sleeveless Anne Klein and I did one hundred sit-ups every night for two weeks.

(Music up: Goldberg Variations #6.)

The night of the party, he found this lovely station on the radio playing Bach and we glided, we swam up from Saddle River toward the country club, not saying a word, just the music between us.

When we got there the first people we ran into were Larry Bridges and his new wife who turned out to be Ethan's girlfriend from Camp Anawana—Beverly.

Beverly was exotic. She drank Brandy Alexanders. She danced. She wore a red dress, too, but next to hers my dress looked brown—almost gray. And she very clearly had something I did not. Beverly had a bosom. It was a nice round bouncy bosom, a melonish kind of loveliness. I wasn't jealous, I was more intrigued. How did one come to have such a bosom? Was it her mother? Did she have sisters? Were they all involved in the bosom business? Or was it just Beverly? I had never seen anything so flawlessly round and so perfectly white in my life. They could have been made of marble.

Ethan stood around and talked to the friends he had stayed in touch with. I said hello to a few people, but mostly I sat at the table, eyeing the fruit cup, waiting for everyone to sit down so we could eat and go home. The shine had quickly worn off the evening for me.

But not for Beverly. She was dancing, she was talking, she was getting around, and making friends with everybody. I lost track of her for a while until she came up behind me, dumped me out of my chair and dragged me over to the bar.

(BEVERLY enters.)

BEVERLY. He looks exactly the same.

BETH. Ethan?

BEVERLY. He still smolders.

BETH *(to us)*. I had never thought of Ethan in fiery terms before.

BEVERLY. Looking at him, you wouldn't know it—but he's not your average kind of guy, is he?

BETH *(to us)*. What was she getting at?

BEVERLY. It just goes to show you—you only know the true nature of a person when you—well you must know.

BETH *(to us)*. No, I didn't know.

BEVERLY. Ethan's the first boy who ever gave me a pearl necklace.

BETH *(to us)*. Who was she kidding? He was from *Poughkeepsie*, his father was an accountant. Pearls? Come on.

BEVERLY. You mean he's never given you one?

BETH. Ethan gives me pens for Mother's Day. One year he gave me a broiler pan for my birthday.

BEVERLY *(intrigued)*. Well, you go right home tonight, and you tell him you want a pearl necklace. You demand that he give it to you. You insist. Besides, you look like you could use it. *(BEVERLY exits.)*

BETH. We went home that night and I drank three cups of Maxwell House while he read the *Wall Street Journal.* When he finally came upstairs, it was after three—but I was up and pumping on twenty-two pistons. As soon as he got into bed, I jumped on top of him and said, Ethan Brown—did you really give that girl Beverly from Camp Anawana a string of pearls?! And suddenly I felt him in between my thighs, get hard like a rock. And I—I started experiencing the most incredible tingling sensation around my chest.

So I said it again:

A string of pearls Ethan, you gave it to her? And now he's so hard, I'm thinking, oh my God, oh my God, oh my God. And he looks right at me, right in my eyes and he whispers: You want a string of pearls?

And I think if *talking* about it is going to get him this hard, imagine what he's going to be like when he gives it to me.

So I say, OOOh, yes, Ethan. You bad boy, you never gave me a string of pearls. I want a string of pearls, give it to me. Wham! He rolls me over, pins me down and rips off my nightgown. His penis is coming out of his pajamas. He throws off his bottoms and pushes me down toward the end of the bed. And the whole time he's saying, You want a string of pearls? You want a string of pearls?

And I'm saying, Yes, Ethan, yes, gimme a string of pearls and the next thing I know he puts his penis between my breasts and whispers,
Squeeeeze it.
OH. OK.
So I squeeze my breasts around his penis.

Now I'm a 34 double A. The only time I ever used a bra was when I was pregnant with Linda. But something happened that night, I swear to God. I touched my breasts and they'd grown. I had mango breasts, beachy Gaugin breasts, breasts like you see in a Renoir painting or a B-movie. I must have been a 40D. Something— something miraculous was happening. He was growing, I was growing, and now he's pumping between my breasts and I'm getting so turned on and he's saying: Yeah, yeah, yeah, oh, baby, oh, oh, oh, uh-hUH, baby, OH OH OHHH!!

And with no warning whatsoever he comes all over my neck. Then he leans over and whispers: "String of pearls."

(Lights up on BEVERLY.)

BEVERLY. When he did it to me I was fourteen.
BETH. Too young.
BEVERLY. Too messy.
BETH. Too surprising.

BEVERLY. Too much work. *(Lights down on BEVERLY.)*

BETH. Two people in each other's arms. That night I fell in love with Ethan and myself—or whoever I thought I was: Barbarella, Kim Novak, Elizabeth Taylor. Surely we all shared something in common now. Finally, I could ask Ethan to put his hands in places I could not say before but could only point to.

And then we began to talk—about his work, about Linda, about the war. And pretty soon, he stopped calling his mother and his brother and he cut off his subscription to *Newsweek* and canceled *Time* altogether and we were really really happy...

And then out of the blue I get this...um, I get this call—the elevator man—the guy who comes in after hours—had found Ethan.

He'd already called the police and they'd told him to call me, so I drove down from Saddle River to Lenox Hill hospital in the city. They told me in the lobby it was an aneurysm and then they let me see him. I remembered picking out the shirt he was wearing at Lord & Taylor. It had been a Father's Day present from me to him, and he'd fought me on the color.

I went home with my little bag of Ethan...a clear blue bag with his wallet, his glasses and his aspirin, and another bag...and inside there was a blue box—square and velvet...

(BEVERLY enters with the box. BETH opens it and removes the string of pearls.)

There wasn't any occasion for it, our anniversary wasn't until October. It was the first time he'd bought me anything for no reason at all and he hadn't even been there to give it to me.

I put the pearls on when I got home. And I wore them to sleep that night and the next...naked except for Ethan's pearls. And that's how I slept for five years.

When my daughter Linda got married I put them in the box and gave them to her.

(LINDA enters and BETH puts the pearls on her. LINDA exits. BETH exits. ELA enters. It is 1981.)

ELA. I knew Linda. We weren't friends, but I knew who she was. She ran the book fair, the bake sale and the Milwaukee March of Dimes Walk-a-thon. She was class parent two years in a row. They called her the Model Mother. No one could touch her. The rest of us were all failures compared to her. When I heard she was moving to Chicago I thought, my God—it'll take six people to replace her.

(We hear the sound of a door opening offstage. Someone is trying to get her attention.)

ELA *(calling out)*. WHAT? No, Carly, you can't come in, dinner's not ready. Because I'm busy. It's not cold out. No it's not, it's above zero. *(The door closes.)*

ELA *(to us)*. Her house sold fast. Too fast. And she wanted her kids to finish school here. That's how she and Amy and Jonathan came to live in my basement apartment. There would be just three of them down there. Howard her husband, was already in Chicago. He planned to visit on the weekends. They paid me the whole six months up front which gave me an excuse to get rid of the last of Billy's things boxed in the basement.

(We hear the door open again.)

ELA *(calling out)*. WHAT? No, Carly, not yet. Chicken fingers and baked beans. Well, then don't put your tongue on the mailbox. *(The door closes.)*

ELA *(to us)*. The idea of someone not related to me living in my house was inconceivable to me—the way the idea of getting a divorce was inconceivable the year before. But you do what you do when you have to do it and like it or not it was done.

She asked me if she could take down the picture of Jesus on one of the basement walls and I let her. I'd had enough of church for the time being anyway. Just a lot of busybodies wanting to hear about Billy. I had no patience so I quit going.

The day Linda moved in, I hid all my jewelry in the freezer and put my silver in the attic. I changed the lock on the basement door and gave her a key; and I finally replaced the burned-out light bulb on the stairs.

Then one day at school one of the mothers—somebody who's never said a word to me in my life—pulls me aside and asks me if it's true— Does Linda Moser have cancer? And I tell her I don't know. Why don't you ask her yourself? And she gives me this look—and then flits off down the hall to ask someone else.

What's she asking me for? Just because the woman lives in my basement apartment doesn't mean I know the intimate details of her life. If Linda Moser has cancer that's her business.

That night around two in the morning, I go down to the kitchen for a Coke and I see Amy asleep at my table. I pick her up and carry her back down to the basement. I look around in the moonlight and I'm pleased to see the apartment looking so clean. I had picked the right tenant that was for sure. Then I laid Amy down in her bed...

(Lights up on LINDA.)

LINDA. Can I have a glass of water?
ELA *(to us)*. And Linda woke up. She had a kerchief around her head but it was half off and there were patches of bald scalp showing.
LINDA. You want to see it?
ELA. See what?
LINDA. My head. I don't mind. I'll show you.
ELA. No. Thanks. No.

LINDA. It's not catching. You can't get what I have just by being in the same room with me.

ELA. I'm perfectly fine being in the same room with you.

LINDA. Then why are you holding your breath? *(Pause.)* Do you want to come to Atwater Beach tomorrow night? There's a group of girls from Shorewood going down there around eight—

ELA. That's not really my kind of thing.

LINDA. You might like it.

ELA. And I don't really know those girls.

LINDA. You might know some of them.

ELA *(lying)*. I'm sort of busy tomorrow night.

LINDA. Then just come for a while.

ELA *(to us)*. I knew I'd be doing her a favor if I gave her a ride. She could always get a lift home from one of her friends. *(To LINDA.)* Sure, I'll take you. *(Pause. To us.)* About a quarter to eight that night I look outside and she's standing by my car wrapped in a blanket.

So I take her to Atwater Beach.

(Lights change. We are at Atwater Beach. WANDA and RANDY enter. Music up.)

RANDY. I'm going swimming tonight.

WANDA. Not me. Too cold.

ELA *(to us)*. I get her settled down in a lounge chair and I'm ready to leave when somebody hands me a drink and then a joint and then a bag of potato chips. I run into some girls I haven't seen since high school.

WANDA. Where've you been, Ela Louise?

RANDY. She's too busy to come see us.

ELA. I didn't know you came here—

WANDA. Sure, sure—

LINDA. I had to twist her arm...

RANDY *(reaches for the joint)*. Hey, twist your arm over here...

ELA *(to us)*. Somebody lights a few candles and the next thing I know it's ten o'clock and I'm drunk and there's this really young cop standing there with a megaphone telling us to disperse or he's going to arrest us.

By then we are two-dozen mostly divorced women in various stages of menopause with seventy-two kids between us and we aren't going anywhere. Somebody threatens to pull the cop's pants down and he gets back in his car.

WANDA. He was cute.

RANDY. Aw, he's leaving.

WANDA. I think he's mad.

RANDY. He wasn't a real cop—was he? *(RANDY and WANDA exit. Music out.)*

ELA. We never see him again. About midnight, I gather up Linda and take her home. We sit on my sun porch for a while, too keyed up to go to sleep. I want to ask her about Howard, about Chicago, about—

LINDA. I taught Amy to swim at Atwater Beach. She was so little but she was so tough, so brave. I think she was just terrified but wouldn't let on. My father was like that. He got quiet when he got scared. Next time we go we should get there early...maybe bring dinner.

ELA *(to us)*. She was talking about next month now.

LINDA. You like roast chicken?

ELA. I don't know.

LINDA. You don't know if you like roast chicken?

ELA. I don't know if I'll go back next month.

LINDA. Oh come on. When was the last time you saw a policeman in his underwear?

ELA. I don't think he'll be back.

LINDA. You never know. *(LINDA exits.)*

ELA *(to us)*. She went down to bed and I didn't see her for a day or two. I thought about the beach— I...I didn't think I would go back. It wouldn't be the same. I'd probably feel uncomfortable. And then, a week later I get a phone call from my sister-in-law Denise.

(Lights up on DENISE.)

DENISE. I heard about these Divorced White Witches from Shorewood who swim naked in Lake Michigan when the moon is full.

ELA. Where'd you hear that?

DENISE. I heard they got a man down there and did something to him.

ELA. Something good or something bad?

DENISE. How should I know? Divorced White Witches swimming naked under the moon? They could have done anything to him—anything.

ELA. What are you telling me this for?

DENISE. You're divorced.

ELA. So?

DENISE. Are you going to go down there next month?

ELA. I don't know, I was thinking about it.

DENISE. I'll go with you.

ELA. I'm taking someone.

DENISE. Swing by here and pick me up.

ELA. You're not divorced.

DENISE. So?

ELA. So call me when you find your husband fucking the baby sitter in your living room. *(Lights down on DENISE.)* When it was time for class pictures Amy went to school without her socks and Jonathan's shirt sleeves were dirty and frayed. The kids looked hungry. Then I caught Carly going downstairs with a frozen pizza. So I started bringing the three of them upstairs for dinner.

(We hear the door open offstage.)

ELA *(calling out)*. Carly, take your mittens and your boots and your coat off right there! RIGHT THERE. Where's your hat? That was a brand new hat! Now you go right back out and find it. Well put them back on. You heard me. Now get OUT! *(The door slams shut.)*

ELA *(to us)*. I was downstairs once when Linda's mother Beth called. Linda never told her how bad things were. She said she'd rather have a good conversation with her mom than a sad one. Howard came to see her but he couldn't sit long. It crushed him, she said, and she needed him to stay whole for the kids.

(LINDA enters.)

It was happening so fast, taking over her body with such a fury... Then Linda asked me to open my house and a flood of her friends came to say goodbye. They came at all hours, day and night and finally I just stopped locking the door.

Soon the only thing that worked were her eyes—they were huge and getting bigger it seemed—you could see her soul pushing through them—trying to leave her body behind, struggling to get out into the air and breathe. She was expanding as she was dying, growing larger instead of smaller. *(LINDA puts the pearls on ELA.)* About a week before she died, she gave me a blue velvet box that had belonged to her mom. It felt strange— I'd seen them on her so many times. When she put them on me, they were so flawlessly round and so perfectly white. I asked if she didn't think her daughter Amy should have them and she said, No, they're for you. For a job well done. And she explained, although very briefly, that her mother had gotten them from her father for the very same reason.

(LINDA exits. Music up. Tiny white lights, insects in the night, flicker on and off around ELA.)

The night after Linda died there was a full moon. We all met down at the beach, the Divorced White Witches of Shorewood, and we took off all of our clothes and we swam naked in the warm lake water. Soon the men came—dozens of them, silent and staring. And as we lifted ourselves out of the water lit by the July moon they bowed to us one by one and kissed our breasts and our hair and we turned them into fireflies that glowed once, twice and were gone. Then we made our way to the towels hanging from the trees and went home to our empty houses.

(The moon begins to fade. The tiny lights flicker out.)

When I started going back to church, I wore them. People would notice and say something nice. I kept the little box on my bureau. All the gold had rubbed off the bracelets and earrings Billy had given me but I didn't care. I had Linda's pearls. I wore them for almost a year rain or shine and then one Sunday—they were gone.

(HELEN enters. She silently takes the pearls from ELA and exits.)

ELA. I tore the house apart—I cleaned out every closet, every shelf, every box in the house—I ripped up half the carpet with a staple remover 'til my hands bled. When Billy called I asked if he'd seen them. He was working in San Diego but had just come home to see Carly. No, he didn't remember seeing any pearls. When I told the Shorewood girls they cried. Some of them came over and we lit candles but it was no use. They were gone. That week some of them chipped in and bought me a little string of pearls at Marshall Field's. Teardrop pearls, you know. Nice. Nicest thing I own.

(We hear the door open offstage.)

ELA *(calling out)*. Did you find it? Well it's out there somewhere. No, no, come in, it's OK. The chicken's on the table. I'll go find your hat. No, no, you sit, I'll go. Because I'm your mother. *(ELA exits.)*

(HELEN enters. She wears a smart black suit and the pearls. It is 1982.)

HELEN. I met Billy at one of Mayor Wilson's parties. They were old friends and the mayor thought he might give us a hand with the Republicans. Wilson was keen on getting the Republican Convention here. Billy had worked with the RNC all over the place and they liked having him around.

At the party Billy and I exchange phone numbers and he comes to my office the next day with a bottle of champagne.

Champagne? I say. Isn't that a little premature? We haven't even filled out the forms.
And he says—Come here, baby, and I'll fill out your forms.

Oh my God, it was so tacky you had to love it.

So Billy basically moves in with me—into my office, into my apartment, we're doing everything but chew each other's food. He's worthless in the office but the staff likes him and my gorgeous new Republican pitch-fuck is about the best-looking thing in San Diego.

When he goes back to Milwaukee to visit his kid, I get a ton of work done. But I miss him, he's cute. Three days later he comes back with pearls. *(She takes them off and runs them over her teeth.)* They're real.

I wear them to work the next day. They actually go nicely with the little black St. John suit I bought in March. It was on sale so I bought two—one for me and one for my sister for her birthday. Stephanie wears sweatpants most of the time.

(STEPHANIE enters.)

STEPHANIE *(to us)*. Where the hell am I going to wear a suit?

HELEN *(to us)*. That's what most of her friends wear: casual clothing at all times of the day.

STEPHANIE *(to us)*. To a party for a five-year-old?

HELEN *(to us)*. I can't imagine what it does to her psyche.

STEPHANIE *(to us)*. To Mommy and Me/Music for the Wee?

HELEN *(to us)*. And I'm far too much in the public eye to even consider it.

STEPHANIE *(to us)*. I don't even get out of the car to go the bank. *(Lights down on HELEN.)* I hate telling people I'm an architect because the next question usually is: What are you working on? And, well, right now I'm working on potty training. I'm mothering. I'm dragging my three-year-old kicking and screaming out of play-dates while she tells me what a horrible mother I am.

(ZOE enters.)

ZOE. I hate you!

STEPHANIE. Fine, but we still have to go home.

ZOE. I hate you, I hate you, I hate you.

STEPHANIE. Zoe, you love Mommy.

ZOE. No.

STEPHANIE. Yes, you do.

ZOE. Mommy?

STEPHANIE. What, sweetheart?

ZOE. Do you like to make drawings?

STEPHANIE. Yes, Zoe, Mommy loves to make drawings. Mommy draws buildings. You've seen Mommy's buildings.

ZOE. Well, I'm gonna tell God to chop off your hands and pull out your eyes so you can never make another building again in your whole life no matter how much you cry.

STEPHANIE *(to us)*. And I think, silly Zoe, God's already done that.

(ZOE exits. Lights up on HELEN.)

HELEN. Did you like the suit?

STEPHANIE. Loved it.

HELEN. Did you try it on?

STEPHANIE. Yes, it looks beautiful.

HELEN. When are you going to wear it?

STEPHANIE. When you get married. *(To us.)* She's been engaged three times and she always keeps the rings. She says that the men insist and I say nobody insists you keep a $10,000 ring. She gets them appraised right away, then she breaks up with them. I'm not saying the two things are related. I'm just saying it's odd.

HELEN *(to us)*. I don't know how she ended up with her husband Andrew. *(Pause.)* Well yes I do know.

STEPHANIE *(to us)*. She never lets me forget that she dated Andrew first.

HELEN *(to us)*. Are you kidding—I gave him to her. I did everything but put a pink bow on his cock. I mean come on she was an architect, he was in commercial real estate. Strip malls. Tulsa. Cigar smoke in the car. They were perfect for each other. *(Lights down on HELEN.)*

STEPHANIE. Last fall, a couple Andrew and I know from Boston wanted to build a guesthouse and they called me. We had a meeting and they gave me a small retainer. That night, I went home, made the kids dinner, tucked them into bed and did thirty-four thumbnail sketches in eight hours.

I woke the kids, took them to school, came home and kept going until the school nurse called to say Dominic had broken his arm in gym. The next day Zoe came down with chicken pox. Then we had a flood in the basement, the dog got hit by a car, and the mommy gerbil ate all the baby gerbils.

I had both kids home on and off for two weeks while the baby sitter was home visiting her sick father in El Salvador. He recovered. I didn't. By the time I went back to my notes and house sketches an entire month had gone by. I looked at what I'd done and it made no sense. It was shit. I sent the check back to my friend and I never saw her again. If my sister only knew...

(Lights up on HELEN.)

HELEN *(to us)*. My sister has it so good she doesn't even know it. I'm days away from the convention pitch and I still don't have numbers from the Marriott or the Hilton—and the people at United who swore up and down we'd get a twenty-five percent discount now say they'll only give us fifteen. And Billy's still around. He hasn't had a single usable idea, not one original thought the entire time, but he keeps second guessing our pitch every five minutes. The mayor calls ten times a day, the printer needs the books by tomorrow, the convention committee wants to know if we can move up the time and Billy loses it. He yells at me, the son of a bitch screams at me in front of my own people—so I kick him out of my office. An hour later the mayor calls and he tells me I'm off the team.

STEPHANIE *(to us)*. The last time I spoke to Helen she sounded depressed. She'd lost a big piece of business and she was actually crying on the phone. Andrew happened to be in San Diego and I asked him to go and see her. Maybe he could make her feel a little better.

HELEN *(to us)*. Stephanie calls me twenty times a day. Am I OK? Am I all right? Doesn't she have anything better to do?

STEPHANIE *(to us)*. Andrew travels two weeks out of the month. He's missed three vacations. They still haven't made him a vice president but they say it's going to happen this year. So he works every night and most Sundays. The kids fight when he's around just to get his attention. But when I complain to him, he says—Hang on. Hang on we're almost there. Keep your chin up, it's just around the corner. We're so close. And what I want to know is, so close to what? Where are we going? Tell me about this mythical place that will erase the last seven years of my life. Because I'm so bored I'm going out of my fucking mind. That's where I'm going. *(STEPHANIE exits.)*

HELEN. Andrew's in town. I meet him at the airport Hilton. He's going on and on about his business but I don't care. He looks good. And after his third gin and tonic he tells me he only wishes he'd met someone like me. Someone independent, someone who had more than diapers on the brain and I say, Well you could have had me.

And he says—Can I have you now?

The next thing I know, I'm paying the check and he's getting a room and we're chasing each other down the hall; I mean he is literally trying to tear off my clothes and just as we get inside the door, he rips my pearls off my neck—Billy the Asshole's pearls break all over the floor. I look over Andrew's shoulder and see myself hovering on the ceiling, watching as he rams himself into me for the seventeenth, eighteenth, nineteenth time—and the woman on the ceiling won't even look at me—she is so disappointed, so disgusted. And I know right then and there that I have pitched my last fuck.

(STEPHANIE enters. She holds up a pearl.)

STEPHANIE *(to us)*. I find a pearl in Andrew's pants while I'm cleaning out his pockets. He'd found it on the plane coming home. So I thread it onto a little string and when Zoe comes home from school, I give it to her and she goes wild for it. She and I get all dressed up and I take her to Antonio's for dinner. My butcher's there getting a pizza and when I say hello he has no idea who I am— me in my St. John suit.

And just as we sit down, I catch a glimpse of a beautiful woman and her little daughter in the mirror across the room—and it takes me a good two or three minutes before I realize—that's me in there. That's who I am. And while we're waiting for our dinners Zoe pulls six colored pencils and a little pad out of her purse and begins drawing. And when I ask her what she's making she says, "A building."

(HELEN and STEPHANIE exit. We hear the sound of a vacuum cleaner running over carpet. Suddenly we hear something getting sucked up into it. The vacuum stops. JOSIANNE enters.)

JOSIANNE. I have two more rooms to clean on the fifth floor and then I can go home. I do not need the Hoover breaking down at this moment.

I open the bag of dirt and pour the dust into a towel, and there is a pearl. Hmm. I will give it to the front desk.

I start the Hoover again, and again I hear something go up into the bag. I open the bag and now there are two pearls inside. I look down at my feet and I see six more. Now I'm on my hands and knees and I find twenty, thirty, forty-two more.

Someone will be missing such beautiful pearls. The guest will call the hotel when they get home and realize they are gone. I will bring them to Mrs. Lawrence, the general manager. Perhaps she will give Albert and me a free dinner for returning them. She did it once for Sarah.

Sarah found a thousand dollar in a drawer. But when I tell Albert on the phone about the pearls, he says to bring them home first. He wants to see them.

I finish cleaning the other rooms. Maria wants to have a drink but I tell her I'm tired and go home. There is a letter from my daughter Nina waiting for me. I have not seen her in twelve years. She is in Tunis with my aunt. I call her once a month.

(Lights up on Josianne's AUNT PATTY.)

AUNT PATTY. Nina can't come to the phone.

JOSIANNE. Is she there?

AUNT PATTY. She's going out with her friends.

JOSIANNE. With a boy?

AUNT PATTY. She's your daughter, what can I tell you?

JOSIANNE. Lock her inside the house.

AUNT PATTY. You had Nina when you were fifteen! What do you expect?

JOSIANNE. *Ou est l'argent que t'envoye?*

AUNT PATTY. Gone.

JOSIANNE. Where?

AUNT PATTY. Where. Money goes. And it goes fast. You think you send so much?

JOSIANNE. Did you go to the lawyer?

AUNT PATTY. With what? He only sees the ones who can pay.

JOSIANNE. I'll send more money.

AUNT PATTY. Much more. We need more.

JOSIANNE. Tell her we'll be together soon. Tell her—

AUNT PATTY. I have to go. My program is on. *(Lights down on AUNT PATTY.)*

JOSIANNE. Hello? Hello? *(To us.)* I call back ten times but no one answers.

In the letter Nina says she has a boyfriend. A boyfriend. A *boyfriend*. Albert comes home smelling of beer and looks at the pearls. He turns them over in his hands. He makes a great show of knowing nothing.

Albert is my brother's friend. I know he tells my family what I do and where I go. I know he is watching me even when I can't see him. I have a cousin in Washington I want to see but he says no. It is too far.

He is the one who brought me to Mrs. Lawrence. She gives him my check. He gives me half, the rest he sends home to my aunt. *(Pause.)* He *says* he sends it home. And for that I have always given him what he wants.

He thinks we can sell the pearls in L.A. I tell him that is stealing. He tells me we have to go to L.A., we have to do this. He makes me think something bad will happen if we don't get rid of them. When I ask him for the pearls back he wraps them in his handkerchief and puts them in his pocket. Come and get them he says. I lock myself in the bedroom and pretend to go to sleep. Albert sleeps on the couch. All night I fix my hair, my nails, my face.

In the morning I put on my dress and Albert puts on his suit and we drive to L.A., to the beach, where the fancy hotels are. He parks the car on the street by the first hotel.

He takes the handkerchief out of his pocket and when I reach for it he slaps my hand away. He tells me to go to the beach behind the hotel; he will meet me there. I want to go inside but he says no. He says I look like a whore. People do not buy pearls from women who look like me. I watch him go inside the hotel with the pearls. Then I follow him in. The hotel has a large and expensive jewelry store on the second floor. Bucheron it says in the window. Paris, Santa Monica, Hong Kong, Sao Paulo.

I go to the beach and I wait. It is very hot. I have no umbrella, there is no shade and I am very tired. I watch a woman and her little girl on the beach. The mother walks away. She gets a Coke, she buys some french fries. The little girl sits there waiting for the mother to come back. *Elle ne bouge pas.* The mother walks further away. She talks to a man, she listens to some music, she goes further down the beach. The little girl waits for her mama. Then someone comes—a man, a woman, I can't see—and throws the little girl into the water. No one on the beach does anything. No one sees the baby drowning. Where is her mother? Where is her mother? *Where is her mother?*

(ERICA enters.)

ERICA. Honey, you're scaring all the kids.
JOSIANNE. That girl is drowning!

ERICA. Which girl?

JOSIANNE. In the water!

ERICA. Where?

JOSIANNE. I have to do something!

ERICA. But nobody's drowning—

JOSIANNE. Out there!

ERICA. There's only children playing. Look!

JOSIANNE *(to us).* She's right. The children are all running back and forth in the water, the mothers are holding the babies in their arms.

ERICA. You want me to get you some water or something? I've got some grapes over at my blanket.

JOSIANNE *(to us).* I see Albert coming. *(To ERICA.)* No, no. Thank you no. *(ERICA exits.)* Albert shows me an envelope of money. Look, he says. Look. Six hundred dollar. The buyer for the whole company was leaving for Paris. He's taking them with him. Albert is very pleased with himself.

I kick him in the balls and I grab the money and I take his keys and I run back to the car. I get in and I drive. Two days and nights I drive and I don't look back until I reach the end of the world. I park and I get out.

Tacoma, Washington, is the ugliest place I ever saw but I stay and I find my cousin and I get a lawyer and I give her my six hundred dollar and I start to get my daughter here. And when she comes, I'm gonna put her in school and I'm gonna lock her up in my house and she's not gonna come out until the day I die. *(JOSIANNE exits.)*

(DORA enters. It is 1983. Music up. WOMAN enters with a jewelry box. She opens it to reveal a strand of white pearls.)

DORA. Cultured pearl.

(WOMAN enters with jewelry box. She reveals a strand of black pearls.)

DORA. South Seas pearl.

(WOMAN enters with a jewelry box. She opens it to reveal a photograph of an eight-year-old girl.)

DORA. French Pearl. *(The WOMEN exit except for DORA. Music out.)* When they interviewed me to be a chaperone, I made it clear to Mr. Martins that I would go wherever the ballet company needed me—any city in any country as long as I did not have to go to France. I was born in Paris and had not been back since I was eight.

When the ballet company toured France they usually took Mrs. Phillips. She spoke Italian and usually got along fine with everybody. Then I got the call from Mr. Martins—an overseas call—telling me that Mrs. Phillips had run off with a Sicilian ticket taker who worked at the opera. I knew he wasn't calling to find out if I'd heard from her. No. He was calling to ask me if I could replace her.

I could have told him no. I didn't need the money. He would have understood, it was last minute. I had a grandchild on the way—two grandchildren actually. Twins run in my family.

But the idea of going to Paris right away, that night, with not enough time to think about the implications or complications did make me slightly giddy. I looked out the window onto Riverside Drive and a limousine was already waiting—apparently for me.

I pack so quickly I forget to bring a book. At the gate I find a *Newsweek* lying on a chair and I take it. As the doors close I read that twenty-five percent of all French believe that Jews are not normal people. Ten percent believe they should be destroyed. I have three Scotches before dinner.

(Lights up on JITTERS.)

JITTERS. Are you nervous?

DORA. A little.

JITTERS. Me, too. My mother gave me a Valium and my father gave me a Valium and my Aunt Frances gave me some codeine. This is my first plane flight and I must have fallen asleep during the take-off because it feels like we're not even moving and I know we must be because they wouldn't have loaded us onto the plane just to have us stand still, you know? You want a Valium? My mother had it blessed by the priest.

DORA. No thank you.

JITTERS. You ever been to Paris?

DORA. A long time ago.

JITTERS. This is my first time. It's great, right? I'm going to study at the school of the Louvre.

DORA. Really? My mother studied at the Ecole des Beaux Arts.

JITTERS. Never heard of it.

DORA. She was a painter.

JITTERS. Yeah, I tried painting and I pretty much suck at it.

DORA *(to us)*. My mother was a gifted painter. My father was her teacher. During the war he hid my mother in his studio outside Paris. When it was over a deranged Frenchman came to my father's town looking for Jews.

A woman and two little girls were the first people he saw. First my mother... *(SFX: gunshot.)* Then my twin sister Pearl... *(SFX: gunshot.)*

JITTERS *(to DORA)*. Hey—are you OK?

DORA *(shook up)*. I have to get up.

JITTERS. Yeah, sure. *(JITTERS exits.)*

DORA. We land in Paris and I am whisked to the Theatre de la Ville where Mr. Martins and the dancers are rehearsing. They are all immensely pleased to see me. When I go to the hotel there are three bottles of Burgundy waiting in my room. A gift from Mr. Martins.

On our day off I go to the Louvre. On the Place Vendome I pass a jewelry store. I glance in the window and there is my sister staring back at me. I blink and she is gone.

I continue to the museum where I come across a portrait of a young girl, a Vermeer called "La dentelliere." It is The Lacemaker. As I look at the portrait, two young people approach me and block my view. I move to get out of their way and they move, too. I step to one side and they step, too. It becomes a kind of game with us.

A guard in a gray uniform comes over and asks us what is the matter. The young people look at me and walk off mouthing something. Breathing it as they laugh out of the gallery they call me "*Juive*." It sounds like a curse or a hex or it is something dirty, obscene. *Juive.* And the guard says nothing.

On my way home I pass the jewelry store again—Bucheron—and this time I go in. A necklace catches my eye in one of the glass cases. I attract the attention of a saleswoman who shows me the strand of pearls on a blue velvet cloth.

(A FRENCH SALESWOMAN enters with the pearls.)

FRENCH SALESWOMAN. A beautiful choice, madame. They are 8740 francs.
DORA. They're lovely.
FRENCH SALESWOMAN. You are American.
DORA. Yes.
FRENCH SALESWOMAN. These came from California a few months ago. From L.A. From a big big Hollywood movie star. I cannot tell you her name. Would you like to try them on?
DORA. May I?

(She puts them on DORA.)

DORA *(to us)*. They are like a kiss on my neck. They are cool and smooth to the touch, like another skin.

There is weight to them, but it is comfortable, regular, like an arm around your shoulder, like someone squeezing your hand.

FRENCH SALESWOMAN. They suit you.

DORA *(to us)*. But before I can answer her, there is an explosion outside the jewelry store. *(We hear a loud explosion. Lights change.)* The security men rush out into the street. The little saleswoman hides behind her counter. *(The FRENCH SALESWOMAN exits.)* There is chaos in the store—people are moving toward the exits. I turn away from the counter and I walk out onto the street. There's a huge cloud of smoke and people covered in blood are sitting on the curb. I hear an ambulance and the scream of a child and I see a woman lying in the middle of the street and there is Pearl, crying, screaming, bending over her body, and this time I take Pearl's hand and we run, *we run*. My father says I'm quick on my feet. He says I've always been fast... Since I was eight...standing on the corner...me on one side of Mama and Pearl on the other... *(DORA opens her palm to reveal the strand of pearls.)* I have always been fast on my feet. *(DORA exits.)*

(VICTORIA enters and climbs a platform. As the lights fade down we hear a splash. Lights up on VICTORIA as she towels herself off. It is 1996. She wears the pearl necklace.)

VICTORIA. We move from St. Louis to New York City. We find an apartment on Riverside Drive overlooking the George Washington Bridge. There are ballet posters on every wall. A pink tutu hangs over the bed. There are piles of New York City Ballet programs in the hall. The apartment comes with everything in it. It takes two Dumpsters to get it all out.

There is a can of Canada Dry Ginger Ale in the back of the master closet. When I lift it, it rattles like there's something inside. I try to open it but the pop-top is fake. There's no ginger ale in it. It's one of those hollow cans people buy to hide their valuables.

I find a hammer in the hall closet and I smash the can— almost too hard—and a pearl necklace falls out. I try to contact the previous owner of the apartment but her number in Austria is disconnected. Her lawyer had let slip during the closing that she had run off with a Viennese ticket taker. I get the pearls appraised and they are worth $5400. I wear them. I've earned them. I gave up everything to come here. Everything, everyone, every joy I had in St. Louis.

We have money now. Alexis attends a private girls' school. Josh orders cases of expensive wine delivered to the apartment. I walk along the river alone. My friends in St. Louis call me less. I try to drown my loneliness in a glass of wine before Alexis comes home. When I complain to Josh that I'm unhappy, he tells me I don't try hard enough.

So the next day I attempt to connect with the mother of a child in Alexis' class.

(ABBY enters.)

VICTORIA. Hi!

ABBY *(trying to avoid her)*. Hi—I've really got to get to work—

VICTORIA. What are you doing for the holidays? I know Alexis would love to have Chase over.

ABBY. We're spending the first week in Woodstock and then we're going to Rome.

VICTORIA. Rome? How wonderful. I love Rome.

ABBY. We're going to see the pope.

VICTORIA. I love the pope.

ABBY. Up close.

VICTORIA. Really—the pope?

ABBY. We have an audience.

VICTORIA. But aren't you—?

ABBY. What?

VICTORIA. Aren't you Jewish?

ABBY. I am Jewish. You can be Jewish and still have an audience.

VICTORIA. By why would you—?

ABBY. Why would I want to see the pope? He's the pope. *(ABBY exits.)*

VICTORIA. I read in the *New York Times* that there is a team at Mount Sinai Hospital making a heart from pig guts. That's what I want, a pig heart. The one I have is too soft. But it won't be ready for another fifteen years so I must do with the heart I have for now. I enroll Alexis in a swim program for underprivileged youth in

Washington Heights. I fill out the forms—I make Josh an electrician instead of an investment banker and I put us on food stamps. I cannot wait until the program begins. Maybe these are the mothers I belong with. Maybe these will be my people.

(VICTORIA stands on the platform. Lights down. We hear the sound of a splash. Lights up on VICTORIA toweling off.)

VICTORIA. I take Alexis to her first lesson. I gaze at the women clustered on the bleachers. I sit alone, calculating. The timing must be right, I must approach them effortlessly. If I look desperate they will sense it and they won't want me.

(CHERYLE enters and sits down near her.)

CHERYLE. I like your pearls.

VICTORIA. I forgot I was wearing them.

CHERYLE. Macy's right? There was a sale last week. I got a string for my mother. They looked exactly like those, except to tell you the truth—I think mine were bigger. Tell me you missed the Macy's sale and I'll just die.

VICTORIA. I missed it, I did.

CHERLYE *(looks out at the swimmers)*. Come on, Valerie! Go! Go!

VICTORIA. Go! Go! *(Beat.)*

CHERYLE. I'm going to the Whitney next week, you want to come?

VICTORIA. Me?

CHERYLE. Unless you're busy—

VICTORIA. I'm not busy. *(To us.)* Her name is Cheryle.

CHERYLE. I figure if you're going to live in the greatest city in the world, you might as well take advantage of it.

VICTORIA *(to us)*. She has little hearts painted on her fingernails and a tattoo on her ankle. Her daughter uses a Playboy bunny towel.

CHERYLE. I like MOMA but lately I've been taking the bus out to Queens to PS 1. I think their collection is improving. Or we can go to the Frick or the Jewish Museum. I can take Mostly Mozart or leave it but I'll stand in line all day for Shakespeare in the Park. As long as I have my *Times* with me. I read the *New York Times* every day cover to cover. *(CHERYLE exits.)*

VICTORIA. Cultured white trash. Tears well up in my eyes. Thank you, God.

(VICTORIA stands on the platform. Lights down. We hear a splash. Lights up on VICTORIA drying off.)

VICTORIA. We get our nails done, we go shopping, we go to MOMA. We have coffee with Theresa who has three kids by three different men. We go to a movie with Kyoko whose English is so bad the cashiers at A&P make sport out of overcharging her. I wear T-shirts with logos and dirty beat-up jeans. I change back to my real clothes in the car when I get home. When Josh asks me why Alexis is swimming in Washington Heights, I tell him I want her to be well rounded. I even give him a picture from one of the meets.

Spring comes and Cheryle and I steal the key to the swimming pool after one of the meets. We start coming down after dinner, after the kids are asleep. We can't get enough of each other.

(CHERYLE enters.)

CHERYLE *(awed)*. You did not finish the *Times* crossword puzzle.

VICTORIA. It's Monday. Monday's easy. Try me on Friday—I get four answers.

CHERYLE. I got a date on Friday. Kyoko fixed me up with her brother.

VICTORIA. Her brother!

CHERYLE. She showed me his picture.

VICTORIA. How's he look?

CHERYLE. Japanese.

VICTORIA. What if you don't like him?

CHERYLE. She says she fixes him up with all of her friends. She'll fix him up with you if you want.

VICTORIA. I'm married.

CHERYLE. So?

VICTORIA. You can't go out with Kyoko's brother.

CHERYLE. He makes good money.

VICTORIA. You're crazy.

CHERYLE. You know what I want to do? I want to get married. I want to wear a white dress and stand up in church and go home with the groom. You were smart. You married an electrician. Never out of work. I should have figured out a way to make more money, you know? Tonight Dougie told me he wants to go to college next year and I don't know how I'm gonna do it.

VICTORIA. Can he get a scholarship?

CHERYLE. For what? Dating?

VICTORIA. You said he's smart.

CHERYLE. He doesn't apply himself. He's like me. I didn't blossom 'til I got to Adelphi.

VICTORIA. You'll figure out something. You're smart.

CHERYLE. I don't know why you think I'm so great.

VICTORIA. You are great.

CHERYLE. No I'm not. I'm just a stupid bitch who likes to swim.

VICTORIA. You're great because you're not going to go out with Kyoko's brother because you don't want to hurt her feelings when he ends up being a jerk. You turned her down, didn't you.

CHERYLE. Fuck you—you fucking mind reader! I'll meet you at the car. *(CHERYLE exits.)*

VICTORIA. Then an article comes out in the *New York Times* about businessmen and their families who support the poor and Josh is in the article. It talks about the job-search project he started for the homeless, and his work for the Parkinson's Unity Walk in Central Park. I'm so proud he's being recognized until it mentions that even his daughter swims with the underprivileged. And there's a picture of Alexis at one of the meets. And then it hits me while I'm reading this that Cheryle is reading it too. *(She removes the necklace. As she says each name, she lovingly looks at a pearl on the necklace.)* Cheryle, Theresa, Kyoko and Carla. Juanita and Malva and Sujita. All the mothers on the swim team—they're all reading it. I take the pearls down to the little park under the George Washington Bridge and I throw them as far as I can into the Hudson.

Then I call Cheryle and I get her machine. Two days go by and she still doesn't call. I go to her house. I sit in her driveway and honk the horn. I call her from my cell phone. I ring the bell. I can hear Pinky, her Jack Russell terrier, barking his head off inside.

(VICTORIA stands on the platform. Lights down. We hear the sound of a splash. Lights up.)

VICTORIA. I have taken ninety-eight dives. Little by little I chisel the women away from my memory. Their faces are already gone.

(Lights down on VICTORIA. We hear a splash. Lights up. She is gone. ABBY enters. It is 2000.)

ABBY. We have this farm up near Garrison—twenty-five acres with a stream. Jake loves it because he can take the kids fishing. I tag along one day and I'm the only one who catches a fish—a huge striped bass. Jake offers to cook it for dinner—he's a much better cook than me. Sometime during cocktails I hear him yelling in the kitchen but he won't let me in. He has a surprise for us. So we all sit down to dinner—my sister-in-law and her kids are with us for the weekend—and Jake comes out with this gorgeous platter of striped bass on a bed of spinach, leeks and what do you know—pearls. Apparently when he'd gutted the fish he'd found a strand of pearls inside. How amazing! How incredible! Everybody thinks it's wonderful wonderful—except my mother. She's such a killjoy my mother.

(GLORIA enters.)

GLORIA. You're not going to eat that fish, are you?

ABBY. It swallowed some pearls, so what?

GLORIA. A fish doesn't swallow something foreign unless there's something wrong with it.

ABBY. You want to analyze the fish?

GLORIA. Pass the salad please.

ABBY. Oh give me a break.

GLORIA. Pardon me?

ABBY. Nothing.

GLORIA *(to an unseen child)*. Sammy, put your napkin in your lap and for heaven's sake sit up. *(GLORIA exits.)*

ABBY. Nobody eats my striped bass after that. Even Jake looks a little nervous. I wrap the pearls in a napkin—the clasp is broken—and stuff it in one of the drawers in the buffet. The next morning I mention to Mom that I'm going to get the necklace fixed; my office is five blocks from the diamond district—

(GLORIA enters.)

GLORIA. You don't think they're real, do you? They're fake!

ABBY. How do you know?

GLORIA. It's so obvious. They're junk. Why else would they wind up in a fish? Oh, my God, Jake—she thinks the pearls are real!

ABBY *(to us)*. Now everyone starts to laugh—

GLORIA. Abby, wipe your glasses.

ABBY *(to us)*. The kids, Jake, my sister-in-law. Everyone's laughing.

GLORIA. Honey—you want pearls, go to Mikimoto. *(To the unseen Sammy.)* Sammy, stand up straight, you're slouching. *(GLORIA exits.)*

ABBY. My mother is so judgmental. She has a comment for everything. Because she's got this ridiculous, highly arbitrary set of standards and precious few things measure up. Precious fucking few.

Five years ago Jake's doing a lot of business in Rome. He pulls some strings and gets us an audience with the pope. I figure this'll shut her up—what could be more impressive, more authentic, than the pope—so I invite her to meet the pope. But she thinks we're kidding. So she doesn't come. We get home, we show her pictures of us with the goddamn pope and she thinks it's hysterical.

(GLORIA enters. She is looking at snapshots.)

GLORIA. He's a fake!

ABBY. Mom, I swear to God—

GLORIA. It's an actor. Where'd you get your picture taken? The Piazza Navona? *(GLORIA exits.)*

ABBY. I show everyone at work and they think it's him. Nobody laughs. I manage 700 million dollars in pension funds. I predicted the market upturn in the fourth quarter last year—and my mother thinks I'm a moron. She makes me give her a key to our apartment.

(GLORIA enters.)

GLORIA. In case I'm on the westside and I want to relax.

ABBY *(to us)*. She has nothing to do, so she goes to my apartment and moves things around. She goes through my closet. And then she goes through the kids' rooms.

GLORIA. Your daughter dresses like a tramp.

ABBY *(to us)*. She hides things she doesn't like.

GLORIA. And your son dresses like a fairy.

ABBY. Ma!

GLORIA. What? *(Beat.)*

ABBY. Never mind. *(To us.)* Then last weekend, she makes us take her up to the country. She loves it up there because the house was built in 1899.

GLORIA. A weekend house should be 19th century.

ABBY *(to us)*. It's a crystal-clear Saturday, the leaves are so green and the water in the stream is deep and blue...

GLORIA. I'm going for a swim. *(Lights down on GLORIA. We hear a splash.)*

ABBY. And she never comes back. She has a massive heart attack. We have to fish her out of the water. No pearls in her gut.

We wait to tell Chase because she's away at sleepaway camp. But Sammy is with us. He's six. I think I should tell him that Gramma decided to leave her body and become a squirrel. But Jake thinks that's too weird because there are so many squirrels on the property. So I tell him Gramma left her body and became a swan. Gramma became a beautiful white swan and swam down the stream and into the Hudson. And maybe—maybe someday she'll visit us again. Oh, he loves that idea.

I know my mother wants her funeral at Frank E. Campbell in New York—very prestigious, very swank, very Mother.

But I decide no, no—there's a funeral home in Mount Ivy—a decrepit little place on Main Street. Let's have the funeral here. *(ABBY exits.)*

(KYLE enters.)

KYLE. I work at the funeral home. People say it looks like a cocktail lounge with a bunch of caskets in back. But Mr. G pays me cash and he's been flexible about my hours since I started caring for my mother.

I bathe her, I dress her, I carry her up and down two flights of stairs. I shave her legs, brush her teeth, change her diaper. She recognizes my sister when she comes to see her. She can tell you what she had for dinner last night, but for some strange reason, she has no idea who I am. My mother thinks I'm her nurse. Every Friday afternoon she tries to pay me.

On Saturdays I take her for iced coffee at Dunkin Donuts. She remembers that she likes Dunkin Donuts.

(KYLE'S MOTHER enters.)

KYLE'S MOTHER. Buy me a donut.
KYLE. Not 'til you say my name.
KYLE'S MOTHER. That honey-glazed one with the pink **sprinkles.**

KYLE. Go on.

KYLE'S MOTHER. Kyle.

KYLE. That's right. I'm Kyle. I'm your daughter.

KYLE'S MOTHER. If you were my daughter you'd buy me that donut.

KYLE. I'll get you the donut, but we gotta wait in line.

KYLE'S MOTHER. I want it now.

KYLE. Mom, we've got to wait in line just like everybody else—

KYLE'S MOTHER. I don't want to wait.

KYLE. Well, you have to.

KYLE'S MOTHER. Something's running down my leg.

KYLE. Now?

KYLE'S MOTHER. Something's going in my shoe.

KYLE. You just peed in the potty two minutes ago—

KYLE'S MOTHER. My socks are wet—

KYLE. Jesus, Ma.

KYLE'S MOTHER. Miss—you gotta take me home. *(KYLE'S MOTHER exits.)*

KYLE. When I break out in hives on my back and shoulders, Dr. Beckman says it's a reaction to my fatigue. He tells me to check Mom into the nursing home in New City, just for a week so I can get some rest. Where am I going to get the money for that? He gives me ointment for my itch and I go home. But the ointment doesn't work and the hives spread to my face and my neck. I'm so nervous. The more nervous I get, the more I itch. I'm getting less sleep now because Mom's waking up at five a.m. And I'm changing her twice before dinner because she keeps shitting herself—

KYLE'S MOTHER *(offstage)*. Miss!

KYLE. My brother loses one of his jobs so he cuts back on what he sends us—

KYLE'S MOTHER *(offstage)*. Miss!

KYLE. We're getting behind on the gas and electric but I make sure she gets clean clothes and her pink donut—

KYLE'S MOTHER *(offstage)*. Miss!

KYLE. And she's still calling me "miss" and this is ten years I'm doing this, ten fucking years. And every night I pray that when I wake up she'll be good and dead—

KYLE'S MOTHER *(offstage)*. MISS!

KYLE. So I can get out of here. *(KYLE exits.)*

(ABBY enters.)

ABBY. Mother needs a suit to wear to her funeral. Even I know that. She has one in a Bergdorf's bag hanging in the back of her closet that she's already bought for the occasion. But I don't really feel like going back to the city. So I go off to Beacon and get a sweet little ensemble at the Salvation Army. Eight bucks. I get her pantyhose at the drugstore in Cold Spring. I find black pumps at Our Lady of Perpetual Help's rummage sale. There's a perfect pair of diamond studs at Woolworth's. Well—they look like diamonds. Then I go home and I lay it all out on the bed and I realize that something isn't right. Something is definitely missing. I fly through the house until I reach the dining-room buffet and when I open the little drawer—there they are.

I run into Garrison and beg the owner of this little jewelry store to put a cheap clasp on them for me overnight. She actually does a nice job.

(JEWELER enters. She gives ABBY the pearls.)

ABBY. How much?

JEWELER. Twenty-five. Are you sure you didn't want a better clasp on there?

ABBY. No. Thanks.

JEWELER. If you ever want to sell them I could give you a good price.

ABBY. For these? They're fake.

JEWELER. Who told you that? Those are perfectly matched rosé pearls.

ABBY. What does that mean?

JEWELER. Spherical, beautiful. High luster.

ABBY. You mean they're real?

JEWELER. You really ought to have a better clasp.

ABBY. Oh my God.

JEWELER. Put them on, I want to see.

ABBY *(puts them on)*. How do they look?

JEWELER. Whoever told you those were fake was crazy.

ABBY. Yeah. *(JEWELER exits.)* I go down to the funeral home.

(Lights up on funeral home. ABBY enters. KYLE enters.)

KYLE. Would you like some time alone with her? I'm done.

ABBY. No. Thanks. I want the casket closed.

KYLE. It must be hard to let your mother go.

ABBY. Oh, it's awful. Imagine your own mother dying ten feet from your house.

KYLE. Yeah. That'd just break me to pieces. *(Beat.)*

ABBY. Thank you. *(She is about to leave then turns back.)* Wait a minute. *(She removes the pearls and gives them to KYLE.)* These are hers. *(ABBY exits. KYLE arranges the pearls on the unseen, dead GLORIA.)*

KYLE. I put the pearls on the deceased. She looks so pretty. That hot-pink blouse around her face and hands makes her seem more vivid. And her shoes—you know they're leather by the way they shine. And look at all that fancy jewelry. Expensive stuff. You know that woman loved her mother a lot to be able to give those things up and not take them for herself. It made me ashamed. My mother deserved someone better than me. *(KYLE exits.)*

(Lights up on CINDY. There is a large pile of dirt next to her. She holds a cellular phone.)

CINDY *(into the phone)*. No, Mr. Krause, the daughter still hasn't arrived, we've been waiting over an hour. Yes, sir, I will, but there's a swan out here about half a row down. It's doing this thing where it comes toward me baring its teeth and then turns around. It's gone back and forth about ten times. What should I do, it keeps getting closer? Yes, sir. Thank you, sir. *(She hangs up.)* I fill in the grave and say a quick prayer. There is no one left to bury today and I have already raked the gravel paths. I had looked forward to having lunch with Mrs. Willow, my third-grade teacher who died last year—aisle 258, section 96, plot 7—but it begins to rain so I take the rest of the day off. I dare myself to go to Wendy's. I gaze at the tables of five and six laughing women having lunch with their friends from work.

Every night I go to the bookstore and stare at women in the aisles. They turn and flee. I sit in the chairs for browsers and stay until closing. I read the books people have left behind. In the last week, I have read *How to Make Your Own Cannon*, a *Field Guide to Mushrooms*, *Attila King of the Huns* and *The Life and Lyrics of Sir Edward Dyer*.

I have a card printed with my name and phone number and have dropped it into every Dostoevsky and Faulkner on the shelves. I've left fliers with my name on it in the bathroom at Starbucks. But nobody calls. Not a single person. I am looking for a woman, but no one is looking for me.

I go to O'Donaghue's for a nightcap. Jerry gives me a beer and then I see her down at the end of the bar. What creature sits before me? What soul from heaven has found me on earth? I cannot take my eyes off this woman.

(BETH enters.)

BETH *(to us)*. I am seventy-four years old and I have never been to a bar by myself. But my granddaughter Amy is still giving me the silent treatment and the television is broken. Six seats down from where I sit there is a woman who weighs at least three hundred pounds. She stares at me all night.

CINDY *(to us)*. I look at her and miraculously she looks back.

BETH *(to us)*. The bartender gives me my Brandy Alexander and says that she is harmless.

CINDY *(to us)*. I go to the bathroom quickly quickly!

BETH *(to us)*. But it is getting late and I have to go home. *(BETH exits.)*

CINDY. When I come back—she is gone. She has left behind a book. It is a book of poems by Sir Edward Dyer. I know this book. I've read this book.

(BETH enters.)

BETH *(to us)*. The next night, I take my red dress from Bonwit Teller out of the closet and I go back to O'Donaghue's Tavern. Amy thinks I am at the Piermont Library taking a watercolor class. But I am really at a bar in Nyack being ogled by a behemoth.

CINDY *(to us)*. She has very blue eyes and small breasts.

BETH *(to us)*. Her nose is sunburned. There is a trace of mud on her shoes—but she has a kind, intelligent face.

CINDY *(to us)*. Jerry gives her back the book of poems. She thanks him. He tells her that I was the one who found it and gave it to him for safekeeping. *(BETH rises.)* Oh my God, she's getting off her stool. Oh my God, she's coming over. She's going to—

BETH. Hello.

CINDY *(to us)*. Her elbow grazes my right pinkie. Every pore in my body explodes.

BETH *(to us)*. She has nice full lips and smells like chocolate.

CINDY *(to us)*. She tells me her name is Beth. She's fifteen years older than me, maybe twenty. Maybe twenty-five. Oh fuck it, she's ancient, but I don't care.

BETH *(to us)*. Cindy's vague about what she does. Something to do with dirt or plantings I think. I tell her about Amy and Kevin and the wedding. I tell her little about myself. What is there to say? The most important thing to happen to me in almost four decades is occurring as we speak. I finish my third Brandy Alexander and I leave. I know Jerry is watering them down and I tip him handsomely. *(BETH exits.)*

CINDY. I go to the bookstore and buy the book of Sir Edward Dyer poems. I start memorizing all of them.

(BETH enters.)

BETH *(to us)*. I see her at O'Donaghue's again the next night and she's very shy, very sweet. I find her rather refreshing in a big sort of way. She asks me if I want to smoke marijuana. *(To CINDY.)* How does it work?

CINDY. You inhale and you keep it in your lungs as long as you can and then you blow it out.

BETH. Then what happens?

CINDY. You feel good for a while.

BETH. How much do you smoke?

CINDY. Quite a lot actually.

BETH. Where do you get it?

CINDY. I grow it. Where I work there's a lot of—land.

BETH. They let you grow it there?

CINDY. Who?

BETH. The people you work with.

CINDY. The people there—?

BETH. Yeah.

CINDY. They're pretty quiet about it.

BETH *(to us)*. She takes me to her car and we smoke the marijuana. I let her touch my breasts. What do I care? It feels good. I am having a wonderful time.

CINDY. "Seas have their sources and so have shallow springs;/ And love is love—

BETH. "—in beggars as in kings." I love that poem.

CINDY. Really?

BETH. Sir Edward Dyer. 1543 to...

CINDY. To 1607.

(BETH exits.)

CINDY *(to us)*. I am drowning in fireworks. I am giddy at gravesites, I have lost all decorum.

(CINDY returns to the cemetery.)

CINDY. Mrs. Willow: I have a love! And she's alive!

(KYLE enters.)

CINDY *(to us)*. I meet my friend Kyle for dinner. She has hives all over her arms and bags under her eyes. *(To KYLE.)* Are you OK?

KYLE. Tired.

CINDY. Kyle, have you ever been in love?

KYLE. I'm not sure.

CINDY. Plato said: "Love is the joy of the good, the wonder of the wise, the amazement of the gods."

KYLE. No, I'd remember that. *(KYLE removes a box from her pocket.)* I'm selling a string of pearls. You know anybody who'd be interested?

CINDY. Where'd you get them?

KYLE. They just sort of…came to me.

CINDY. How come you're selling them?

KYLE. So I can put my mom in a nursing home in New City and take a vacation.

CINDY. Where are you going?

KYLE. To sleep.

CINDY. I could buy them. I could give my love a token of my affection. How much?

KYLE. Seven hundred.

CINDY. That's a lot.

KYLE. OK, $650.

CINDY. $675.

KYLE. Cindy. Don't be an idiot. *(KYLE gives her the box.)*

CINDY *(to us)*. I go to the bank and take the money from my savings account and I give it to Kyle. The Grand Canyon of Hope has no bottom. *(CINDY exits.)*

KYLE. I take the money and I put my mom in a nursing home and I go to sleep for a week. When it's time to pick her up, she's waiting for me at the front door with a young man, an orderly. The minute she sees me she grabs his arm and says—That's her. That's my daughter. Kyle. I pick up her suitcase and lead her to the car; I've got a honey-glazed donut with pink sprinkles waiting for her in the back seat. And we go home. *(KYLE exits.)*

(BETH and CINDY enter.)

CINDY. I have something for you.

BETH *(to us)*. A gift?

CINDY *(to us)*. My heart is thudding in my chest—

BETH *(to us)*. She's half my age.

CINDY *(to us)*. Sweat is running down my armpits—

BETH *(to us)*. I have no gift for her.

CINDY *(to us)*. She opens the box.

BETH *(lifts the pearls out) (to us)*. Is it possible? No. Once love is gone it doesn't come back. But they are so flawlessly round and so perfectly white. Suddenly I am so sure that these are my pearls.

CINDY *(to us)*. That's all she says.

BETH *(to us)*. I know these are my pearls.

CINDY *(to us)*. And then she begins to cry.

BETH *(to us)*. I know that if I tell my granddaughter Amy, she will think I am crazy. But I am so sure. And as I sink deeper into the person I forgot I was, there is Cindy sitting next to me... After so many years, could this be...?

CINDY *(to us)*. She is speechless.

BETH *(to us)*. Love?

CINDY *(to us)*. And she is so beautiful and soft I make love to her.

BETH *(to us)*. And I let her. *(CINDY puts the pearls on BETH and exits.)* I toy with the idea of keeping them. The next night, I take off all my clothes and I get into bed with only the pearls. But there is no thunder, no earth shakes below me. Ethan doesn't come to me in the middle of the night. In fact, I have a very odd dream; I dream that Amy and Kevin have a baby, which is silly because I know they have no intention of having children.

I take the silence and the dream together as a sign and the next morning I knock very softly on Amy's door.

(AMY enters. BETH puts the pearls on her.)

AMY *(to us)*. I am getting married.

BETH *(to us)*. She is wearing my pearls.

AMY *(to us)*. Gramma thinks they're mom's pearls—her pearls.

BETH *(to us)*. She doesn't believe me.

AMY *(to us)*. I want to believe her. *(BETH exits.)* She is so sure. Does it matter? I wear them with my wedding dress— which I finish the night before—

(BETH enters on CINDY's arm.)

And I marry Kevin, though I am certain as I walk down the aisle that all eyes are not on me, but on Gramma who is on the arm of a very large and much-younger woman. *(CINDY exits.)* Kevin and I spend a week in Maine and then it's back to work. I am instantly pregnant and—we are overjoyed. Delirious. *(AMY exits.)*

BETH. Cindy and I baby-sit for my great-granddaughter, Lily. We play hide and seek. For years we play.

And then one day I see Lily in the kitchen holding a cookie in one hand and the string of pearls in the other and I want to tell her to be careful. I want to tell her that she is holding something very precious in her hand. But she will only think that I am talking about the cookie.

Then before I can say a word, she waves at me, sails out the door and is gone. *(Lights down.)*

THE END